WONDERFUL WORDSMITHS

Edited By Jenni Harrison

First published in Great Britain in 2022 by:

Young Writers
Remus House
Coltsfoot Drive
Peterborough
PE2 9BF
Telephone: 01733 890066
Website: www.youngwriters.co.uk

Printed and bound in the UK by BookPrintingUK
Website: www.bookprintinguk.com
YB0496E

FOREWORD

For Young Writers' latest competition This Is Me,
we asked primary school pupils to look inside
themselves, to think about what makes them unique,
and then write a poem about it! They rose to the
challenge magnificently and the result is this fantastic
collection of poems in a variety of poetic styles.

Here at Young Writers our aim is to encourage creativity
in children and to inspire a love of the written word, so
it's great to get such an amazing response, with some
absolutely fantastic poems. It's important for children to
focus on and celebrate themselves and this competition
allowed them to write freely and honestly, celebrating
what makes them great, expressing their hopes and
fears, or simply writing about their favourite things.
This Is Me gave them the power of words. The result
is a collection of inspirational and moving poems that
also showcase their creativity and writing ability.

I'd like to congratulate all the young poets
in this anthology, I hope this inspires them
to continue with their creative writing.

CONTENTS

Highfields Primary School, Lawford

Jessica Page (9)	68
Orlaith Taplin (9)	70
Maya Pearson-Smith (9)	72
Harriet Marshall (9)	74
Milo Chatwin (9)	75
Ava Mason (9)	76
Jack Voller (9)	78
James Talbot (9)	80
Sophie Allwood (9)	82
Caitlin Sanders (9)	83
Jack Galvin (9)	84
Finley Wrycraft (10)	85
Edward Simmonds (9)	86
Bentley Hadland (10)	87
Miley Carrington (9)	88
Joshua Lampard (9)	89
Gabrielle Parkes Van Rooyen (9)	90
Ruby O'Riordan (9)	91

Lenham Primary School, Lenham

Molly Root-Hicks (8)	92

Southmead Primary School, Wimbledon

Aneela Rauf (10)	93
Ryan Oghenekevwe (10)	94
Joshua Elston-Giroud (10)	96
Hanan Sidhu	98
Charlotte Dzienisiewicz (9)	99
Nabiha Khalid	100
Sofia Sheikh (10)	101
Hanaan Omar (10)	102
Shayla Payne (8)	103
Lorenzo Worrell (8)	104
Aemilia Ambroseprieto (10)	105
Dua Zahra (9)	106
Haris Ahmed (10)	107
Karis Jenner (10)	108
Charlieann Aiyegbeni	109

Fiona Springer (8)	110
Josh Herron (11)	111

St John's CE Primary School, Kearsley

Theo Davies-Cooper (7)	112
Mariya Rashid (7)	113
Delilah Degney (7)	114
Alice Marland (8)	115
Jabir Muhud (8)	116
Jakob McGuire (8)	117
Evie Martin (7)	118

The Cardinal Wiseman Catholic School, Greenford

Aleksandra Wolodzik (11)	119
Milosz Szczęsny (12)	120
Enzo Florece (11)	123
Panashe Mhembere (11)	124
Noah Vita (12)	126
Alicja Zywiecka (11)	128
Gisela Rodrigues-Ram (12)	130
Caywen Estibeiro (12)	132
Adam Gallagher (11)	133
Flossie O'Meara (11)	134
Ruby Lynch (11)	135
Mariam Albazi (11)	136
Maja Adamczyk (11)	137
Scarlett Awad (11)	138
Ksawian Thisokkumar (12)	139
Izabela Salo (11)	140

Winston Way Academy, Ilford

Sara Khan (10)	141
Nishwanth Patro (11)	142
Dia Zareeta Hossain (10)	144
Aishah Arif (10)	145
Mehdi Shah (10)	146
Raina Morshed (9)	147
Durva Kore (9)	148
Zara Gir (10)	149

THE POEMS

Ozzie Oh Ozzie!

You silly, silly dog!
You run so far, don't you?
First you roll in puddles,
Then it's fox poo!
I know you're not any wiser,
But come on!
You can run for miles without getting tired,
Yet you can still wake up at dawn.
Sometimes you're lazy and sometimes you're not.
You're like a cat that curls up in a chair.
The thing is, you're not as graceful as a cat though.
More like an old man with a face full of hair!
But that is just you.
A dog that needs shampoo for the fox poo!
Ozzie oh Ozzie!

Grace Harrison (10)
Argyle Primary School, Camden

The Greek Rhyme Of A Myth

A boy named Theseus lived with his mother.
His dream was seeing the king, also known as his father.
When he saw his father, he looked confused.
Of why fourteen Athenians had been used.
Theseus and them were demanded by Theseus' father,
To go to the labyrinth and kill or rather,
Slay a Minotaur near King Minos' palace.
Theseus got excited and made a promise.
Off went the people sailing to Crete,
Where if a black sail comes it shows Theseus had been defeated,
Minos' daughter devised a plan,
To give Theseus a sword and thread as Theseus ran.
Theseus was out of breath when the Minotaur roared,
But didn't stop Theseus to stab with his sword.
With the minotaur dead in the lair forever,

Theseus sailed back to Athens after.
But Theseus forgot to change the sail to white,
The king was upset even though it's not right,
The king killed himself curled up like a pea,
That is now known as the Aegean sea.

Ayan Haque (10)

Argyle Primary School, Camden

My Name Is Ibtisam

My name is Ibtisam,
I am a funny little girl,
I've got a bossy sister and a helpful brother,
You wouldn't want to have another,
They are a lot to me,
I really like everything I see,
I've got a lot of friends at school,
They say I am the kindest of the rest,
They help to keep me grounded,
And that is me.

Ibtisam Abdirahman (9)
Argyle Primary School, Camden

Be Your Dream

To make your dreams come true,
There is lots you have to do.
Not worrying about what other people think,
Because they will be gone in a blink.
Having fun in all you do,
Will make you happy and get you through.
Always try your best,
Then you won't be stressed.
Determination is the key,
Put in the work and you will be buzzing like a bee.
Never giving up,
Until you win that cup.
When you fall down,
Get back up and don't frown,
Family and friends are all around,
Cheering you on in the crowd.
Being who you truly believe you can be,
Comes from the heart of me.

Amelia Coulstock (7)
Belmont Mill Hill Prep School, Mill Hill Village

Who Am I?

My name is Poppy
It means flower
Gorgeous red petals, carpeted with power,
Drama, English, and climbing, these are my
passions
I am also quite into wearing the latest fashions
I want to be a warrior, to stop and do what's right
To make sure everybody gets a future where they
are full of delight
My favourite colour is green, used to be pink,
It is the best colour, I used to think
I have lots of friends, more than you might guess
I have drifted away from some of them, I must
confess!

I have a passion for writing, you know
Even outside in the cold snow!
The crunch of it under your feet,
Still gives me a lovely burst of heat.
I have uncles and aunties
One of which is very arty!
I am a person who will always stand up for other
people's rights

Just to give them a happy burst of light!
I care for others,
I haven't even any brothers!
I am as cool as a block of ice
Many try to sprinkle me with a lot of spice
But I will not flare up, burn my surroundings
And give everyone a pounding.

I can be naughty at times,
But I would never commit a crime
I can also be sassy,
But at the same time, quite classy!
Let's focus on my good traits now,
But I am not the cat's meow!
I have a lot of empathy, which is good,
At least I am not alone in the woods.
My heritage is from India and Scotland
But hopefully they will both get a bit more
grassland!
I would like to become an actor
And escape from common factors.
I believe everybody should be treated like equals,
And it should carry on, in a sequel.

I am a person who believes in a pure world
Carpeted with green, and seas that whirl
Where there is no abuse or violence
And we are all proud as lions.

I have a love for acting,
I just find maths distracting.
I love cracking mysteries
And finding out about history
I hate hockey
It makes my insides go chalky
As soon as I hear silence I go deathly cold and
white,
It just gives me quite a fright!
I'm not perfect, nobody is
It makes me feel like a quiz
All of this is who I am,
And I always try to be the best I can.

Poppy Wrench (10)
Belmont Mill Hill Prep School, Mill Hill Village

This Is Me

My name means water,
I am my family's youngest hopper.
I'm as tall as a massive hall.
My senses are good so I can hear far away calls.
I look like wheat which makes roti
That I like to eat.
I am grateful that I have a life
Which challenges me every day
To thrive.
I like to play football
Even though I fall.
I am helpful as a reliable friend
And that's by being loyal to take up their stand.
I'm not dumb and raise my thumb
To a growth mindset.
To others I am no bully
And I treat them respectfully.
I love my traditions
That come in each season.
My creativity is at Lego
That sparks my ego.

When I'm old
I will be good as gold
For the work I'll do will be kind
Which will always stay in everybody's mind.

Neer Somaiya (8)

Belmont Mill Hill Prep School, Mill Hill Village

This Is Me!

I make people happy,
I have a good personality.
I always look smart,
I have a fashionable heart.
I am kind,
And never leave my friends behind.
I like to stand out,
So, I don't need to hide.
I am strong,
Stronger than King Kong.
I am the shepherd,
Not the sheep,
I always like to take a big leap.
When I am older,
I want to box,
In the ring I want to knock people out of their
socks.
In my extra time I like to bake,
From a chocolate sponge to a lemon drizzle cake.
I am good at cricket,
Can smash a ball for a six,

I can bowl out one by one,
Some from the keeper catching nicks.
I want to be famous and want to become a
billionaire,
And finish my list by throwing hard-earned money
in the air.
I will end up victorious,
I will always stay glorious.
This is me.

Laksh Somaiya (11)

Belmont Mill Hill Prep School, Mill Hill Village

Hope

I am Asha; my name means hope
Hope means to dream; dreaming is a vision
A vision of a world around me.

But the world around me is dying
Dying in pain
Will I experience the world that awaits me
Before it's all gone in vain?

I hope to climb majestic mountains
Before the glaciers melt away
I hope to see frozen icebergs
Before they break away.

I hope to feel dusty desert breezes
Before they're too hot to bare
I hope to breathe fresh forest air
Before rainforests are too rare.

I hope to hear ferocious lions roaring
Before they become extinct
I hope to see enormous elephants stomping
Before they're all gone in a blink

I hope to watch pink flamingos swooping
Before they're too dehydrated to fly.
I hope to smell fields of bluebells blooming,
Before they droop and die

So now you know how my dreams live within me
So now you know who I am
So now you know how hope is me
After all, Asha is who I am.

Footnote: Asha is a girl's name of Indian origin. Derived from Sanskrit, Asha means "wish", "hope" or "desire".

Asha Patani (9)
Belmont Mill Hill Prep School, Mill Hill Village

Wonderful Me!

To create beautiful, wonderful me, you will need:
1. A bucket of wildness,
2. A chunky book of bright, neon colour.
3. A fairy flick of boringness.
4. A pinch of lying.
5. Fifteen giant-sized packets of cookies.
6. Every lost animal in the universe.
7. An endless supply of joy and happiness.

First chuck in the fifteen packets of giant-sized cookies,
Then pour in the bucket load of wildness.
Get a fairy to flick in the boringness.
Then you need to add in a pinch of lying.
Tear in the pages of bright neon from the book.
Last but not least, break in the animals, joy, and happiness.

Halle Pike (9)

Federation of Beckwithshaw Community Primary, Kettlesing Felliscliffe Primary & Ripley Endowed Primary, Beckwithshaw

Something You Should Know About Eliza

I love Lego and my awesome 3D pen
Favourite hobby gymnastics
I can do the splits
Of course I'm very energetic
I love Rebels.
Favourite colour red
Favourite subject maths
Everyone knows I love Nutella!
I'm like a lion and a sheep
Because I'm lazy and brave
Hot pepper - a little bit of this and that
If I was a car I would be a Lamborghini
Blue-green-brown marbled eyes
Dancing and singing I love
My hair is brown with tiger stripes of blond
Favourite book? Harry Potter.
I'm very protective, bullies beware!

To create me you will need
- A 3D pen
- 7 blocks of Lego
- 1,000,000,000 handfuls of happiness
- A drop of sugar
- 4 handfuls of adventure
- 8 lions
- 7 sheep
- 6 bags of pasta

And that's me!

Eliza Haywood (9)

Federation of Beckwithshaw Community Primary, Kettlesing
Felliscliffe Primary & Ripley Endowed Primary, Beckwithshaw

This Is Me!

To create me you will need:

- An Unspeakable-filled house,
- A slab of cheese pizza,
- 10lbs of mischief and fun,
- A pinch of madness and excitement,
- A bucket of glee,
- A sprinkle of maths and science,
- A drop of infinite space and planets.

First you need an Unspeakable-filled house.
Then add a slab of cheese pizza.
Next 10lb of mischief and fun,
A pinch of madness and excitement,
A bucket of glee, a sprinkle of maths and science
and a drop of infinite space and planets
Then you mix it all together left and right
Then you have me.

Kaycie-Jade Rushworth-Clarke (10)

Federation of Beckwithshaw Community Primary, Kettlesing
Felliscliffe Primary & Ripley Endowed Primary, Beckwithshaw

Ava's Dreams

I would like to be a clothes designer.
I pick good clothes - some sparkly and some plain.
I need to choose fabric,
Before everyone complains.
I need a shop to keep my clothes safe
And I must learn how to sew.
There is lots of stuff I need to get,
And things that I don't know.

I'm so excited about my dream,
And making lots of money.
I hope I'll make some lovely clothes,
And still be very funny!

Ava Baron (7)

Federation of Beckwithshaw Community Primary, Kettlesing
Felliscliffe Primary & Ripley Endowed Primary, Beckwithshaw

Me, I, My, Mine

F un sport
O ne of my hobbies
O rganised
T ackle
B all
A ttack
L eeds United
L ove of the game.

G oalkeeper
O bjective
A gile
L egit goalkeeper
K ey tactic
E lliot
E xcellent
P ower
I ncredible in the air
N othing's getting past me
G loves.

G oal

O n top of the world

A mazing

L ive and breathe football.

Elliot McElhatton (10)

Federation of Beckwithshaw Community Primary, Kettlesing
Felliscliffe Primary & Ripley Endowed Primary, Beckwithshaw

No Word Of A Lie

I could eat a pizza as big as a circus tent and that's no word of a lie.
I can do one thousand tricks in one second on the trampoline and that is no word of a lie.
I can play video games for so long that my TV set starts smoking and that is no word of a lie.
I can spin the roundabout as fast as I can jump on it and that is no word of a lie.
I can fly over the beach as fast as a plane and that is no word of a lie.

Luke Munro (7)

Federation of Beckwithshaw Community Primary, Kettlesing Felliscliffe Primary & Ripley Endowed Primary, Beckwithshaw

This Is Me

Thousands of triple chocolate cookies
Helpful - in any way you want
Inspired by others and heroes
Super soccer star

I'm extremely keen and dedicated to football
Super soccer saver

Mega fun in the sun
I'm mE and it's great to be me.

Hugo Pike (10)

Federation of Beckwithshaw Community Primary, Kettlesing
Felliscliffe Primary & Ripley Endowed Primary, Beckwithshaw

No Word Of A Lie

I can cover the whole earth in Nutella and that's no word of a lie.
I can eat all the food in McDonald's without being sick and that's no word of a lie.
I can buy a trillion puppies with 1p and that's no word of a lie.
I can pet a million cats in one second and that's no word of a lie.
I can draw a billion hours a day without getting tired and that's no word of a lie.

Frankie White (9)

Federation of Beckwithshaw Community Primary, Kettlesing Felliscliffe Primary & Ripley Endowed Primary, Beckwithshaw

No Word Of A Lie

I can eat a million burgers at once and that's no word of a lie.
I can read a whole book in one second and that's no word of a lie.
I can solve a maths equation in zero seconds and that's no word of a lie.
I can write the longest word ever in one second and that's no word of a lie.
I can run as fast as Sonic around the world, in one second, and that's no word of a lie.

Eddie Mansfield (8)

Federation of Beckwithshaw Community Primary, Kettlesing Felliscliffe Primary & Ripley Endowed Primary, Beckwithshaw

Something You Should Know About Me

I delight in dancing and
Singing, challenging homework
Loving - I am loving.
And Minecraft is my game.

Friendly
Caring
Very smart - a clever cucumber - yum!
Trustworthy
Wishful
I adore Labradors
And baking
Favourite colour lilac
If I were an animal I'd be a sheep.
An energetic sheep!
This is me
And I'm not changing me.

Isla Williams (9)

Federation of Beckwithshaw Community Primary, Kettlesing
Felliscliffe Primary & Ripley Endowed Primary, Beckwithshaw

No Word Of A Lie

I can eat one hundred packs of raspberries in two seconds and that's no word of a lie!
I can say one billion words in one second and that's no word of a lie!
I can eat all the food in the world and that's no word of a lie.
I watched a hundred hours of YouTube and that's no word of a lie.
I have all of Harrogate as friends and that's no word of a lie.

Billy Parr (8)

Federation of Beckwithshaw Community Primary, Kettlesing Felliscliffe Primary & Ripley Endowed Primary, Beckwithshaw

No Word Of A Lie

I can eat a pancake as big as my house and that's no word of a lie.
I held a handstand for all my life and that's no word of a lie.
I played with Luke on the moon until the sun came out and that's no word of a lie.
I could eat a never-ending salad and that's no word of a lie.
I could ride my bike all around the world and that's no word of a lie.

Angel Newby (8)
Federation of Beckwithshaw Community Primary, Kettlesing Felliscliffe Primary & Ripley Endowed Primary, Beckwithshaw

No Word Of A Lie

I can ride 200 ponies in one second and that's no word of a lie.
I can eat 2000 chocolate bars in one second and that's no word of a lie.
I can eat 1000 Big Macs in one second and that's no word of a lie.
I can eat 10,000 burgers in one second and that's no word of a lie.
I can eat 200 bags of apples in two seconds and that's no word of a lie.

Brooke Ryder (8)

Federation of Beckwithshaw Community Primary, Kettlesing Felliscliffe Primary & Ripley Endowed Primary, Beckwithshaw

No Word Of A Lie

I made my own album and it went viral and that's
no word of a lie.
I can eat a whole pot of Nutella in one second and
that's no word of a lie.
I can buy a thousand dogs every day and that's no
word of a lie.
I made a friend in every single country and that's
no word of a lie.
I drew a thousand people in one second and that's
no word of a lie.

Erika McElhatton (8)

Federation of Beckwithshaw Community Primary, Kettlesing
Felliscliffe Primary & Ripley Endowed Primary, Beckwithshaw

No Word Of A Lie

I am the greatest football player in the world and that's no word of a lie.
I won fifty games in a row and that's no word of a lie.
I jumped one billion feet in the air and that's no word of a lie.
I ate fifty burgers in one second and that's no word of a lie.
I can swim two million lengths in a minute and that's no word of a lie.

Seb Bate (7)

Federation of Beckwithshaw Community Primary, Kettlesing Felliscliffe Primary & Ripley Endowed Primary, Beckwithshaw

Football

F uture star,

O n top of the world,

O ver the moon when I score.

T op of the table,

B ehave ref!

A gile and amazing,

L eeds are the best,

L egit footballer.

G o for goal,

O n the right wing,

A ccurate when I shoot,

L ove the sport.

Ben Hunn (9)

Federation of Beckwithshaw Community Primary, Kettlesing
Felliscliffe Primary & Ripley Endowed Primary, Beckwithshaw

No Word Of A Lie

I can stay under icy water my entire life and that's no word of a lie.
I can do one million backflips and that's no word of a lie.
I can eat a trillion Big Macs and that's no word of a lie.
I can run around the entire world in one second and that's no word of a lie.
I can do one billion pushups and that's no word of a lie.

Ralph Walker (7)

Federation of Beckwithshaw Community Primary, Kettlesing Felliscliffe Primary & Ripley Endowed Primary, Beckwithshaw

No Word Of A Lie

I have 100,000,000 puppies and that's no word of a lie.
I can eat 100,000 peas in one second and that's no word of a lie.
I can play a game in one second and win and that's no word of a lie.
I could learn maths in one second and that's no word of a lie.
I could drink hot chocolate in one second and that's no word of a lie.

Reuben Pallagi (8)

Federation of Beckwithshaw Community Primary, Kettlesing Felliscliffe Primary & Ripley Endowed Primary, Beckwithshaw

No Word Of A Lie

I can win twenty games I fail two times and that's no word of a lie.
I can eat 100 billion nuggets and two Big Macs and that's no word of a lie.
I can watch TV forever and that's no word of a lie.
I can game my whole life and that's no word of a lie.
I can run on the whole world in one minute and that's no word of a lie.

Theo Hughes (7)

Federation of Beckwithshaw Community Primary, Kettlesing Felliscliffe Primary & Ripley Endowed Primary, Beckwithshaw

No Word Of A Lie

I have bought every teddy in the world and that's no word of a lie!
I bought every single iPad in the world and that's no word of a lie!
I can eat 60,000 marshmallows and that's no word of a lie!
I climbed every tree in the country and that is no word of a lie!
I played every game in one second and that's no word of a lie!

Emerald Wise (8)

Federation of Beckwithshaw Community Primary, Kettlesing Felliscliffe Primary & Ripley Endowed Primary, Beckwithshaw

No Word Of A Lie

I painted a whole room with Nutella and that's no word of a lie!
I can eat 9,998 Big Macs in one go and that's no word of a lie!
I can break bedrock in Minecraft with water and that's no word of a lie!
I can buy 100 dogs with £1 and that's no word of a lie!
I can jump over 10,000 cats and that's no word of a lie!

Alfie Mansfield (8)

Federation of Beckwithshaw Community Primary, Kettlesing Felliscliffe Primary & Ripley Endowed Primary, Beckwithshaw

Achieve Your Dream

Hey!
Ambition, aim, dream, intention, success, faith,
excellent.
When you have an opportunity strive and achieve.
Have self-belief.
I want to be a football goalkeeper.
Imagination, it's no lie.
Use aspiration
Work for it and never give up.
Have faith.
Everyone is ambitious.
Hope, equipped, aim, effort.

Ellis Mackintosh (10)

Federation of Beckwithshaw Community Primary, Kettlesing
Felliscliffe Primary & Ripley Endowed Primary, Beckwithshaw

This Is Me!

To create me:
First, preheat your Disney-filled bedroom

Ingredients:
- A slab of barbecue chicken pizza
- 10lbs of mischief and fun
- A pinch of madness (excitement)
- A bucket of wildness
- A sprinkle of brightness
- 1000 tablespoons of magic
- A cup of joy
- One teaspoon of freckles.

Niamh Smith (9)
Federation of Beckwithshaw Community Primary, Kettlesing
Felliscliffe Primary & Ripley Endowed Primary, Beckwithshaw

No Word Of A Lie

I can drive one hundred cars in a minute and that's no word of a lie.

I can run a marathon in a minute, and that's no word of a lie.

I can skip 40000 times and that's no word of a lie.

I can eat 10,000,000 sweets and that's no word of a lie.

I can run past 50,000 countries and that's no word of a lie.

Sophia Morris (8)

Federation of Beckwithshaw Community Primary, Kettlesing Felliscliffe Primary & Ripley Endowed Primary, Beckwithshaw

You Be You!

Hey!
Roses are red, violets are blue,
I want to play football, do you?
If you want to be a singer remember to be you.
If you want to be a pet shop owner remember to be you.
If people are mean stick up for yourself and show how ambitious you are!
Only you can be you,
I want to play football, do you?

Isabelle Summers (10)

Federation of Beckwithshaw Community Primary, Kettlesing Felliscliffe Primary & Ripley Endowed Primary, Beckwithshaw

No Word Of A Lie

I like playing with alligators and sloths and that's no word of a lie.
My dog can wrestle ten gorillas in ten seconds and that's no word of a lie.
I like watching Space Jam in space and that's no word of a lie.
I can go to every McDonald's in one minute and that's no word of a lie.

Mimi Mackintosh (7)

Federation of Beckwithshaw Community Primary, Kettlesing
Felliscliffe Primary & Ripley Endowed Primary, Beckwithshaw

No Word Of A Lie

I can sing better than Bob Marley and that's no word of a lie.

I can bounce higher than ever and that's no word of a lie.

I can run half a mile and that's no word of a lie.

I can climb the highest and that's no word of a lie.

I can live in a tent and that's no word of a lie.

Kayden Stead (8)

Federation of Beckwithshaw Community Primary, Kettlesing Felliscliffe Primary & Ripley Endowed Primary, Beckwithshaw

Dream Big

Hey! You!

Look I want to be,

I want to be a golfer hitting them balls straight past the fairway onto the green.

My vision is better than an eagle eye soaring through the sky.

I get my driver out and drive for perfection

I want to be better than the best.

Achieve.

Believe.

Have hope.

Harry Greenwood (9)

Federation of Beckwithshaw Community Primary, Kettlesing Felliscliffe Primary & Ripley Endowed Primary, Beckwithshaw

What Makes Me Myself

I like doing art or baking
Painting flowers is my thing
Baking cakes is my thing too
I like to draw random things like doodles or
anything
I am very happy
Playing with my siblings is what I have to do
I sometimes even babysit them
I like chocolate a lot
And that's me!

Daisy Walker (9)

Federation of Beckwithshaw Community Primary, Kettlesing
Felliscliffe Primary & Ripley Endowed Primary, Beckwithshaw

A Rap Poem About Me

I love to do art, I love to sing.
I love to do those things.
When I go out in the morning
A happy feeling pops in my head and I like it a lot.
When I see someone sad
I like to dance to make them happier and to enjoy themselves.
When I am enjoying myself it makes me happy.

Freya Foy (7)

Federation of Beckwithshaw Community Primary, Kettlesing
Felliscliffe Primary & Ripley Endowed Primary, Beckwithshaw

My Ambition

To be a farmer and own my own farm
And learn how to drive the tractor.
I need my dad and granddad
To help me and give me experience.
What will stop me is a cow kicking me and
breaking my leg.
The animals that I want on my farm are
Cows, sheep, hens, a dog, and a horse.

Isaac Ryder (10)

Federation of Beckwithshaw Community Primary, Kettlesing
Felliscliffe Primary & Ripley Endowed Primary, Beckwithshaw

No Word Of A Lie

I ate one million pancakes in one minute no word of a lie.
I can build a house in one second and no word of a lie.
I can eat one million McDonald's in one second and that's no word of a lie.
I can stick Nutella on the walls in one minute and no word of a lie.

Ella Heard (7)

Federation of Beckwithshaw Community Primary, Kettlesing Felliscliffe Primary & Ripley Endowed Primary, Beckwithshaw

My Mystery

I like to jiggle and wriggle
I like to smile
I like being funny
And I can run for miles!

I love banana sandwiches
And I like to dance around
I'm as clever as a sheepdog
And sometimes I can't be found.

Who am I?

Hannah Metcalfe (8)

Federation of Beckwithshaw Community Primary, Kettlesing
Felliscliffe Primary & Ripley Endowed Primary, Beckwithshaw

Most Creative Director

T all and talented
H ungry, as I can be
I t is my dream to be a director
S uper cool.

I maginative
S uper excited.

M orning and night
E very day dreaming of being a director.

Zaak Millum (9)

Federation of Beckwithshaw Community Primary, Kettlesing
Felliscliffe Primary & Ripley Endowed Primary, Beckwithshaw

YouTuber

Y ouTube is what I like
O ld stuff, can't be used
U seful stuff, to help me learn,
T ime, wasted on YouTube
U nbelievably cool
B est website ever
E ntertaining
R eally amazing tool!

Xavier Fordham-Dilasser (9)

Federation of Beckwithshaw Community Primary, Kettlesing
Felliscliffe Primary & Ripley Endowed Primary, Beckwithshaw

All I Should Believe

A ll I want to do is be a caring Christian
O rbiting my friends like planets
I would like to make dreams come true
F amily and friendship forever
E arth holds our feelings and returns our favours.

Aoife Whitfield (8)

Federation of Beckwithshaw Community Primary, Kettlesing
Felliscliffe Primary & Ripley Endowed Primary, Beckwithshaw

Rosie

R oses, daisies, all flowers I like

O bviously I like swimming and gymnastics

S uper at sewing just like my best friend, Evie

I nspired by digital art

E njoyable moments spent with family.

Rosie Porter (9)

Federation of Beckwithshaw Community Primary, Kettlesing Felliscliffe Primary & Ripley Endowed Primary, Beckwithshaw

Gaming!

G aming is the best

A nd lots of fun

M y mum and dad have never tried playing games

I love it so much, it is my life

N ever am I going to stop gaming

G aming is the best.

Barnaby Kirby (10)

Federation of Beckwithshaw Community Primary, Kettlesing
Felliscliffe Primary & Ripley Endowed Primary, Beckwithshaw

This Is Me

To make me you'll need:
- A handful of annoying
- A pinch of naughtiness
- A book of gaming
- A bag of cookies
- A cauldron of focus
- A slice of basketball

And this is how to make me!

Theo Edwards (10)

Federation of Beckwithshaw Community Primary, Kettlesing Felliscliffe Primary & Ripley Endowed Primary, Beckwithshaw

Harriet's Poem!

T all and talented
H elpful Harriet
I nteresting every day
S uper funny.

I nnocent
S uper brainy.

M ad every day.
E xcited.

Harriet Morris (11)
Federation of Beckwithshaw Community Primary, Kettlesing
Felliscliffe Primary & Ripley Endowed Primary, Beckwithshaw

Mysterious Me

I'm as clever as a scientist,
With glasses and brown hair,
So healthy, tall, and friendly,
For my friends I really care.
I'm adventurous and smart,
and a school lover too.
Who am I?

Seth Jones (8)

Federation of Beckwithshaw Community Primary, Kettlesing
Felliscliffe Primary & Ripley Endowed Primary, Beckwithshaw

My Favourite Things

My friends are Mia and Willow
In autumn when it gets dark I like camping
And toasting marshmallows
My brother and daddy camp with me
And sometimes my mummy but she's not very
keen.

Jemima Kirby (8)
Federation of Beckwithshaw Community Primary, Kettlesing
Felliscliffe Primary & Ripley Endowed Primary, Beckwithshaw

My Dream!

S uper cool and amazing

I am skilled

N umber one in the charts

G o to Hollywood

I n a Porsche

N ow packing

G reat future.

Florrie Glendinning (9)

Federation of Beckwithshaw Community Primary, Kettlesing
Felliscliffe Primary & Ripley Endowed Primary, Beckwithshaw

This Is My Me Poem

I am tan
I am smart
I hate fast roller coasters
I love Minecraft
I love my birthday
My name is Peter
I love my mum
My favourite colours are red and gold.

Peter Godley (7)

Federation of Beckwithshaw Community Primary, Kettlesing
Felliscliffe Primary & Ripley Endowed Primary, Beckwithshaw

Singers

S pectacular

I mpressive

N atural singers

G rand

E verything amazing

R eally good

S omeday you could be one too!

Sophie Russell (10)

Federation of Beckwithshaw Community Primary, Kettlesing Felliscliffe Primary & Ripley Endowed Primary, Beckwithshaw

This Is Me

I'm...
Usain Bolt in football boots,
A wonderful winger,
A farm animal lover,
I'm a St. Bernard big and strong
And in running I never go wrong.

Jack Metcalfe (10)

Federation of Beckwithshaw Community Primary, Kettlesing
Felliscliffe Primary & Ripley Endowed Primary, Beckwithshaw

62

No Word Of A Lie

I eat 200,000,000 KFCs and that is no word of a lie.
I like sun lounging, that is no word of a lie.
I kissed too many dogs and that is no word of a lie.

James MacEwan (8)
Federation of Beckwithshaw Community Primary, Kettlesing
Felliscliffe Primary & Ripley Endowed Primary, Beckwithshaw

Who Am I?

I have yellow hair and I am smart
I love to do maths and English
I am awesome at riding my bike
Lime green is my favourite colour
Who am I?

Lewis Williams (7)

Federation of Beckwithshaw Community Primary, Kettlesing
Felliscliffe Primary & Ripley Endowed Primary, Beckwithshaw

I Am Me

I love swimming

A lways happy
M usic liker

M ore family to love!
E veryone's so happy.

Ethan Wilkinson (9)

Federation of Beckwithshaw Community Primary, Kettlesing
Felliscliffe Primary & Ripley Endowed Primary, Beckwithshaw

All About Me

E xcellent at sewing
V oice that is good at singing
I deas always pop in my head
E lephants are my favourite animal.

Evie Broodbent (9)

Federation of Beckwithshaw Community Primary, Kettlesing
Felliscliffe Primary & Ripley Endowed Primary, Beckwithshaw

Nancy World

I love pizza
I love to play
I'm cute
I'm kind and caring
I love Coke
I love to cook and want to be a chef.

Nancy MacEwan (11)

Federation of Beckwithshaw Community Primary, Kettlesing
Felliscliffe Primary & Ripley Endowed Primary, Beckwithshaw

This Is Me

I can hit a ball for miles,
All the way to the River Nile.
I can sing like a bird in the morning dew,
I'm like me and not like you.

I can create an awesome picture,
I can also make a yummy mixture!
My dog is gold, his eyes are black,
He has blond curls on his back!

I can chat all night and day,
(About anything, by the way!).
My hair is chocolate, my lips are roses,
I love learning about RE, especially Moses!

Stroking my cat always makes me feel better,
Also I like to write very long letters!
I love strawberries, especially home-grown,
I can also climb a tree all on my own!

I can be a star if you give me a chance,
I could go on TV performing a dance.

I can make the world's best dinner,
When it comes to swimming, I'm a winner!

Just you wait and see, I'll show you,
This is me.

Jessica Page (9)
Highfields Primary School, Lawford

Happiness Is Me

I'm brave like a lion
Hunting down their prey.
I'm a singing bird in winter
Snow melting away.

I'm an animal lover, my favourite
Pet is a dog called Weston like
A fluffy pompom.

My hair is brown
As chocolate brown
My eyes are marble green
I can make a yummy dish
With my mum, dad, and sister.

I love learning about Islam with
One of my favourite teachers
Mrs Meaking
I love learning about English with one
of my favourite teachers Mrs Wilton
This is my life.

My friends Sophie and Ava are
The best in the world.
I love to sing with my girls
They're the best in the world.
My family love me and I love them.

My favourite season is winter when I
Can have a bonfire and snuggle up on
The sofa. My friend Ruby, who is like a gem,
Delicate and beautiful.

Orlaith Taplin (9)

Highfields Primary School, Lawford

Me .

I'm sweet, I'm sour,
Depending on the hour.
I'm sociable, I'm lonely,
Because I'm the one and only.

Oversized clothing,
Cooking, sailing,
Riding on my bike,
Are all the things I like.

One eye a crocodile-green,
The other a faded blue,
My hair is a light blonde.
I have no favourite song.

I like climbing trees,
But I don't like bees,
Music is my thing,
I kind of like to sing.

I used to have a budgie called Bertie,
And I have a cat that is very furry.

I really love to lie in bed,
But I have nothing to be said.

I like to go skating,
My hands always shaking.
I am a dolphin in the glistening ocean,
When I start to swim.

I would like to know about you too.

Maya Pearson-Smith (9)
Highfields Primary School, Lawford

Harriet And Harriet

Harriet and Harriet, best friends from the start,
Something that day must have clicked in our hearts.
All the way from my crazy school reception,
Year Four in isolation, now that was an exception.

She always looks out for me, cares for me and teaches me a new sport every day.
We have a friendship like no other and I wouldn't have it any other way.

We share the same name, the same golden hair colour, and the same love for sports,
From football to cricket grounds, tchoukball events, and even being on tennis courts.

Together we are a caring, crazy duo that paints rainbows wherever we walk,
If you ever feel low please stop, wave, and feel free to talk.

Whether it's Haz, Harri, or Harriet,
She has always been my female chariot.

Harriet Marshall (9)
Highfields Primary School, Lawford

This Is Me!

I'm a superstar rockstar on a big drum kit,
I'm a mini monster midfielder on the football pitch,
I have blue eyes like the clearest ocean all
together,
I'm a tchoukball chomper (I never miss a ball),
I am strong and brave but definitely a whopper
wasp avoider.

I'm a good team leader but I'd never stand down a
McDonald's,
I'm a book reader, my favourite's Mr Gum,
I'm a chocolate eater, my favourite's milk.

I'm a night owl, I never go to sleep,
I'm a very good animal lover as I have a bunny
called Cosmo.
My name is Milo and I'm very chatty as I'm a
Chatwin,
And I'm very masculine.

Milo Chatwin (9)
Highfields Primary School, Lawford

What's Special About Me?

I can be a swimmer,
Though I may not be a winner,
I love being with my fish,
I can also make a yummy dish.

I'm a real animal lover,
And I'm a big fan of my brother,
I love playing games,
But my brother plays with his trains.

My dad loves his work,
Though he's always out on the search.

My eyes are as shiny as pebbles,
Though my brother is a real rebel,
Music is my leisure,
But my photos are my treasure.

I am very brave,
And I sing like a wave,
My favourite weather is when it's snowy,
And I love sitting on the sofa feeling all cosy.

My friends are as lovely as flowers,
Even in torrential showers.

Don't let emotions get you down!
This is me!

Ava Mason (9)

Highfields Primary School, Lawford

This Is (Sometimes) Me

Artistic, intelligent,
And a cuddler of bears.
Sprouts and grapes,
But not any pears.
No boring brothers,
Yes to red,
And sherbert lemons,
A warm messed up bed.
Slow like a sloth,
But clever like a crow.
Focused, lover of jellybeans,
Disliker of snow.
Special, unique,
Chocolate and drawing,
But sometimes I can
Get a little bit boring.
Chewing nails,
But not any gum.
Bad at sports,
At home I am glum.
Funny and smiley,

As bright as a star,
Eyes of mud puddles,
Liker of old cars.
Js, creativity,
Interested in kings,
Jubilant and laughing,
Nice when clanky bells ring.
Early riser,
Birthdays and being happy,
Delicious cheese crackers.
This is sometimes me!

Jack Voller (9)
Highfields Primary School, Lawford

This Is Me!

I am as caring as a doctor,
As brave as a police officer,
I am a lover of animals,
Roger the rabbit being my favourite.

I am an early riser,
As busy as a bee,
I am an ecowarrior,
Out with my pick-up stick,
Litter, you won't get past me.

My eyes are as blue as the ocean,
Legs as long as a giraffe,
Master at Titanic knowledge,
As funny as a clown.

I'm as happy as the sun,
My favourite subject being history,
I'm as smart as a dictionary,
I'm as powerful as an Egyptian god.

I'm as fast as Usain Bolt,
I make wishes come true,
I'm a shooting star,
That's me!

James Talbot (9)
Highfields Primary School, Lawford

Sophie's Hopes And Dreams

I want to be a reckless rugby player,
I want every player to fear me,
I want to be a terrific tri scorer,
That would make me happy.

I want to have a fashion-forward future,
I want to have delightful designs,
I am also very kind.

I want to be a veterinary nurse,
Or a famous singer or dancer and have lots of
money in my purse,
Helping animals on the go,
Even though I have a dog called Solo.

I want to be a comedian making people laugh,
Or a zookeeper filling a crocodile's mud bath.

There is one more thing I would like to be,
And that is me!

Sophie Allwood (9)
Highfields Primary School, Lawford

Me

I'm a star at jumping on a trampoline.
I love to eat lots of ice cream.
I am an animal lover,
But I am really happy being on my tablet, going on one app to another.

I do not like getting out of bed.
But I really hate banging my head.
My favourite colour is pink because the colour's quite bright.
I like to be in my car at night.

I like to play squash because it is really fun,
But I don't like football because I always score none.
I love lots of music,
But I mostly like the top picks.

Caitlin Sanders (9)
Highfields Primary School, Lawford

What's Special About Me

I can make a good friend,
But I do go through tough bends.
I am proud to be who I am.
I love a good pizza, especially with ham.
I am a caring person.
You will see that I am me.

I can be a hard worker,
But when it comes to dictionary day, I am not a
good searcher.
I am as kind as a vet,
And I like pets.

I am a heavy sleeper,
But I'm not a good leaper.
I am a raging self-defence learner,
But I'm not a wood-burner.
My hobby is being a gamer,
But I hate being an entertainer.

Jack Galvin (9)
Highfields Primary School, Lawford

My Life

Goose - my honking hound
Stealthily stealing socks
Growling like a grizzly bear
Sonorous sounds of snoring
Moaning mischievously for marvellous food.

I'm a tsunami warrior defending the goal
I'm a lucky left winger that plays my role
I can rainbow flick over the school
But sometimes I stupidly lose my ball.

I'm the master carp-slayer reeling in fish
A new PB would be my biggest wish
I go overnight fishing with my dad
But sometimes I'm silly and he gets mad.

Finley Wrycraft (10)
Highfields Primary School, Lawford

My Favourite Things

I love to eat yummy pizza and it makes me happy
I also love a piece of chocolate but it could make
me gappy
I'm a husky lover but I'm a spider fearer.

Maths is my superpower, I love my times tables
I am always in sports clothes with the fancy labels
My best friend is Theo and we love to play football
We even made up a new game and called it
Wallball.

These are just a few of my favourite things
And all that my crazy life has to bring.

Edward Simmonds (9)
Highfields Primary School, Lawford

Me!

I am a...
Terminating bounty tackler in rugby boots,
Husky lover until they blow their coats,
Owner of glistening blue eyes of the ocean,
Film lover with a great imagination,
Lover of the colour gold,
Hater of games that are old.

Heavy sleeper who does not like to be disturbed,
Gets annoyed by a bird,
Owner of a bearded dragon called Sarg,
Scaler of a climbing frame that is large,
Lover of my family,
This is me!

Bentley Hadland (10)
Highfields Primary School, Lawford

Who I Am!

Sometimes I'm funny
Because I eat all the gummy.
I don't read books because
I like to have the looks.

I'm like a turtle
And my favourite colour is purple.
When I go to town
I like to wear my gown.

I like to play netball
Spaghetti bolognese, I eat it all.
I like to have a toffee
When I'm drinking my coffee.

I like to play with Elisha
Because I beat her.
I play with Harriet
Because she's my chariot.

Miley Carrington (9)
Highfields Primary School, Lawford

Miraculous Winger

I fly down the RW like a falcon
A lifelong football fan
I go to matches whenever I can
I am a sporty player.

A superstar singer
I love to play the guitar
A big McDonald's fan
I eat the food whenever I can.

I run like a cheetah
I love to score goals
I am a strong tackler
I like to stay up late.

I love to do PE
And I love to play football
So that is me
The Miraculous Winger!

Joshua Lampard (9)
Highfields Primary School, Lawford

My Magical Future

I have a fashionable future with stylish designs,
I like nature-themed things like ecological vines,
I have artistic skills,
I have two amazing cats,
I hope that one day I get a white parrot and a rat.

Halloween is coming soon,
I'll fly with birds by the moon,
Swimming in lakes is a fun thing to do,
The colours that represent me are yellow, white,
and blue.

Gabrielle Parkes Van Rooyen (9)

Highfields Primary School, Lawford

This Is Me!

I am as caring as a doctor
I am as smart as a border collie
I am as kind as summer
I am as happy as the sunshine.

I am an animal lover
(Lenny the puppy is my favourite).

I am a book with words
I am a world with colour.
I am a flower with all the pink petals on my head.
Last of all a lovely singer!

Ruby O'Riordan (9)
Highfields Primary School, Lawford

Music Rocks

Mindfulness
Sad songs
Sweet songs
Singing in my head
Use it when you are sad
Living without it
Impossible
Can you feel it hit your soul?

Molly Root-Hicks (8)
Lenham Primary School, Lenham

My Personality Recipe

To create me you will need:
- A unicorn and rainbow filled planet
- A bucket full of girliness syrup
- A pinch of happiness and helpfulness
- 20lbs of textbooks
- A handful of fried chicken
- 1000lbs of laughter and fun.

Now you need to...
Add your unicorn and rainbow planet you just made.
Add a pinch of happiness and helpfulness.
Mix! Mix! Mix! As it starts to fade.
Next add 1000lbs of laughter and fun.
Keep on mixing as it starts to shine like the sun.
Stir the 20lbs of turquoise textbooks then you'll start to cook.
Put it on a baking sheet and cook it in the oven.
Wait for it to cool down and add the syrup.

This is me!

Aneela Rauf (10)
Southmead Primary School, Wimbledon

My Darting Dreams

I hope my day will get any better
I live in this two-storey house
What should I do?
I don't know
But I am a big boy
I really should do that stuff.
Play football? Nah.
Play volleyball? Nah.
Play tennis? Never.
I am starving.
Pancakes, ooh, my type.
I want boiled butter
To go on it you know.
Now I'm okay but wait,
There's tea over there, maybe
This is a dream day.
Supper first. Okie dokie.
Knock knock.
"Who is there?"
"Me, your friend, remember?"
"Oh yeah, let's play."

We played through the night.
Until I heard "Good night"
My friend was gone.
I felt tired. I got my phone,
In bed. Bye and sweet dreams.

Ryan Oghenekevwe (10)
Southmead Primary School, Wimbledon

Me - A Stew!

You will need:
- 1000lb fun and laughter
- 600kg Lego and toys
- 1,000,000 tonnes Minecraft and Roblox
- 10 miniguns
- 10 A1M1 Abrams tanks
- 20,000lbs food (any)

- 1 big spoon
- 1 large oven
- 1 ginormous pot.

Method:
Firstly, lob in 500lb of fun and laughter.
Secondly, add that 600kg of Lego and toys.
Thirdly, throw in 1,000,000 tonnes of Minecraft and Roblox.
Then, chuck in those miniguns and tanks.
Finally, add 20,000lbs of food.
After, put on fire and stir until rainbow.

Once it has come out, sprinkle in the other 500lbs of fun and laughter,
And there you have it, a me stew.

Joshua Elston-Giroud (10)
Southmead Primary School, Wimbledon

Which Creature Would You Be?

Which creature would you be?
Today I'll be a chameleon.
I can camouflage like air through the sky.

The little, slow chameleon hides in logs.
Who wouldn't want to explore the home of a chameleon?

It eats with its long, sticky tongue.
It looks everywhere with its beady eyes, so watch out.

They change colour like a rainbow.
If anything gets too close it will hide by climbing a long, thick tree.

It will eat like a lion. It eats leaves and insects.
Who wouldn't want to live this legendary life?

This is me.

Hanan Sidhu
Southmead Primary School, Wimbledon

A Horse

Which creature would you be?
Today I'd be a strong stallion,
Galloping as fast as a hyena.

I love to go "Neigh, prrr!"
It's my favourite thing.
I'm as cute as a fluffy baby polar bear,

I'd love to roam the fresh fields,
For pristine grass.
I would like to be black and white,
With a perfect pink nose.

A horse,
As funny as the best comedian in the world.
I always want to be the top horse.
Now all I do is,

Wake up.
And know that I am with you,
And writing this poem.
So have you made up
Your mind?

Charlotte Dzienisiewicz (9)
Southmead Primary School, Wimbledon

Terrifying, Tremendous Tiger

Which creature would you be?
I'd be a tiger! A terrifying, tremendous tiger.
In the morning, I'm out hunting for breakfast
With my precious family.
I run as fast as a Bugatti.
A hunter tracking its prey.
As powerful as a bear's claw.
Teeth as sharp as a cat's nail.
Face as free as a jaguar.
I go "Roar!" when I see my bounty.
Pow! as I attack my prey.
My breath smells like a dead fish.
But I clean it with some water
From the green river.

Nabiha Khalid
Southmead Primary School, Wimbledon

This Is Me

Amazing animals that steal away your attention
I don't think I even need to mention
The small, blue bird snuggling on my shoulder
She is so cute I just want to hold her
The comforting arms wrapped around me softly
She always has time to spend
And always a hand to lend.
I love all of my fantastic friends
The wonderful books that make your hair stand on end
Delicious pancakes, tasty and chocolatey,
Topped with only the best ripe, red strawberries
I am a lover of most kinds of tea.
This is me.

Sofia Sheikh (10)
Southmead Primary School, Wimbledon

Flying Joy

I am butterflies in your tummy
You are eating all the yummy
The majestic stars who look from upon the sky
Aroma has such an amazing scent that it makes
you fly
All the money that you spent without a pause
Just remember it was for a good cause
All separation must drop
A valiant voice calling out stop
Freedom! Freedom! Freedom!
Shines on the world
The laughter around you hurled
Into your soul
It's never dull
This is me.

Hanaan Omar (10)
Southmead Primary School, Wimbledon

Shayla's Interesting Poem

Say to others, "Well done!"
Help others, and be kind!
A brave girl always says I can do it!
You and I will be best friends.
Love yourself and be positive.
A girl is always a lovely girl.
You're brave, you're strong, you're kind,
And you're unique,
And you'll always be you!
Just make sure you always remember you're kind,
Positive, and have a growth mindset,
Not a fixed one.
Oh! Don't forget to be nice to others.

Shayla Payne (8)
Southmead Primary School, Wimbledon

My Magic Box

Based on 'The Magic Box' by Kit Wright

I will put in my box
A PS5,
The smell and taste of smooth melted chocolate,
With twenty ice creams.

I will put in my box
Magical airforces,
Yummy, beautiful, delicious chocolate fountain,
And beautiful, glorious, nice clothes.

I will put in my box
Lots of fruit, bouncy trampolines,
And shiny, sparkling 500,000 pounds.

Lorenzo Worrell (8)
Southmead Primary School, Wimbledon

All About Me!

I am the purr that soothes your soul.
I am the cuddles that make you lull.
I am the object that melts in your mouth.
Before travelling all the way south.
I am the four-wheeled object that you put on your feet before you travel in a beat.
I am the player who bashes the buttons for a win.
I am the painful pinch that sinks into your skin.

Aemilia Ambroseprieto (10)
Southmead Primary School, Wimbledon

Peregrine Falcon

Which creature would you be?
Today I'd be a peregrine falcon
Like Sim Joustant the most powerful knight in the kingdom
A peregrine falcon who roams free
In a world of clouds structured like a city

Today I will roam free
Today I will be crazy as a prisoner
Which creature would you be?

Dua Zahra (9)
Southmead Primary School, Wimbledon

Our Earth

Why do people keep destroying the Earth?
Deforestation.
Cutting trees is not fine
If we keep doing this we will not be able to breathe.
Rubbish in the ocean will kill animals.
We all have to stop this, please.
Save the Earth!

Haris Ahmed (10)
Southmead Primary School, Wimbledon

Family

F illing your tum with a yummy recipe
A mazing cousins having fun with me
M y secrets kept forever
I am the purr that comforts them
L ove showing the way
Y our beautiful voice showing our joy.

Karis Jenner (10)
Southmead Primary School, Wimbledon

My Pink World

For breakfast I eat pink toast and honey
I swim with mermaids in the pink, sparkling water.
Eating a pink KitKat chocolate bar.
Listening to I Want To Be A Billionaire.
At night I sleep on my pink rubber duck
Drifting into the sun.

Charlieann Aiyegbeni
Southmead Primary School, Wimbledon

The Marvellous Poem

Marvellous poem, marvellous poem,
What are you about?
Cars or bunnies or dogs or frogs,
Monkeys or donkeys,
Oh, just anything or anyone.
Marvellous poem,
What are you about?

Fiona Springer (8)
Southmead Primary School, Wimbledon

The Lovely Poem

I am a Mario player
I am a cat lover
I am a dog owner
I am a Nintendo Switch gamer
I am the fur that strokes me
I am the love in your heart
I am me.

Josh Herron (11)
Southmead Primary School, Wimbledon

Introducing Theo

I am amazing and a good friend
I am brave and brilliant and beautiful
I am cool and creative
I am dashing and determined
I am exiting and a fast eater
I am funny and fun and fair
I have a joy and jolly
I am happy and silly
I am loyal and loving
I am cool, safe, and strong
I am caring and weird and good
I am fearless and grateful
I am a good family member
I am playful and make me smile
I am respectful and ready.

Theo Davies-Cooper (7)
St John's CE Primary School, Kearsley

Introducing Mariya

I am amazing and awesome.
I am brilliant and brave.
I am clever and creative.
I am delightful and dashed.
I am exciting and elegant.
I am fantastic and focused.
I am giving and grateful.
I am happy and honest.
I am independent and imaginative.
I am polite and helpful.
I am cheerful and supportive.
I am rising and ready.
I am silly and making people smile.
I am respectful and kind.

Mariya Rashid (7)
St John's CE Primary School, Kearsley

Introducing Delilah

I am amazing and awesome.
I am brilliant and brave.
I am clever and creative.
I am determined and delightful.
I am exciting and elegant.
I am fantastic and forceful.
I am great and giving.
I am happy and honest.
I am independent and imaginative.
I am jiggly and jolly.
I am clever and kind.
I am loyal and loving.
I am magic and magnificent.
I am nervous and noble.

Delilah Degney (7)
St John's CE Primary School, Kearsley

Introducing Alice

I am funny and loving.
I am sneaky and kind.
I am fun and a reading lover.
I am smart and chatty.
I am caring and creative.
I am nice and helpful.
I am animal friendly and playful.
I am cool and focused.
I am a listener and a helper.
I am a gamer fan and I like music.
I am a nature lover and a weird person.

Alice Marland (8)

St John's CE Primary School, Kearsley

Introducing Jabir

I am awesome and brave,
I am helpful and excitable,
I am funny and friendly,
I am kind and respectful,
I am smiley and safe,
I am weird and silly,
I am strong and polite,
I am happy and focused,
I am cheery and amazing,
I am creative and brilliant,
I am speedy and playful,
I am super and speedy.

Jabir Muhud (8)
St John's CE Primary School, Kearsley

Introducing Jakob

I'm amazing and awesome.
I'm brave and beautiful.
I'm crazy and creative.
I'm determined and a daredevil.
I'm educated and excited.
I'm funny and focused.
I'm grateful and giving.
I'm healthy and helpful.
I'm independent and a bit insecure.

Jakob McGuire (8)
St John's CE Primary School, Kearsley

Introducing Evie

I am loving but cheeky.
I am playful but silly.
I am funny but nice.
I am creative but chatty.
I love family and friends.
I love healthy but unhealthy.
I am strong but cheeky.

Evie Martin (7)

St John's CE Primary School, Kearsley

All About Me

Welcome everyone, boys and girls,
The show is about to start,
Get ready for the poem so sit up straight,
Get ready because the adventure is to begin.

Hello everyone it's Aleksandra here, but you can
call me Ola for short,
As you can see, I am a very energetic girl and I love
active sport.
After school clubs, football, fitness, and drama are
all my type,
Although all sports I really like.
I go to Scouts, which is very fun and exciting too,
Making fire, sleeping in tents, many games, and
something new.
As you can see,
I can be a busy bee.
Or I could be a little lazy like a sloth,
Or I could just be both.

Aleksandra Wolodzik (11)
The Cardinal Wiseman Catholic School, Greenford

My Tremendous Life

Once I arrived,
I was ready to thrive,
But nature had to strike me,
Without a cure.

Given the deadliest medicine in the world,
Told to cure my disease.
Parents thought it was going to be fine as gold,
'Till things took the wrong turn.

Perhaps overdosed by the NHS,
Or born profoundly deaf,
In order to survive
The danger I was being put in.

It felt like sitting on a pin,
For twenty-four hours,
Hospital bed I was put in
Spending the next week in hospital without power.

Getting ready for the lifechanging plan
And finally...
It began.

New magnets with wires implanted into my head
within two surgeries.

Three long months later,
Switched on with sound processors.
Hearing the first time my name has been told...
It was a gift from God.

A new life was waiting for me...

Two whole years later,
Start of primary school,
This experience was much greater,
Can't say I didn't feel like a fool.

Soon after nursey was the start of reception
Learning my ABCs and 123s
New friends and a good education was a
temptation.

Year One and Two passed within a breeze
And that was it of KS1
KS2 - feelin' like a champion with no disease
It felt like my education was done.

This time has come - Year Six - top of school,
Filled like an ocean
My era to rule;
Words can't describe my emotions.

Holidays I'll never forget approach
New house purchase
Steady like a roach
Not an easy purchase because of the service.

At the same time,
A new high school had to be located for me,
For my next six years of life to not commit a crime
We found one right by the sea.

And it was the perfect house!

This is me, Milosz!

Milosz Szczęsny (12)
The Cardinal Wiseman Catholic School, Greenford

I, Enzo

Hello there, my name is Enzo,
I am fast and furious and I like to eat Freddos,
I like to play hockey and I'm pretty good at it,
My friends know about it and they think it's super lit.
I also play the piano and the violin,
Whenever I'm in a contest I will always try to win.
I'm a very friendly kid who loves to play with his friends,
One of the cars that I want is a Mercedes Benz.
I'm very, very smart, and I like to make poems,
I like the book Artemis Fowl, with fairies, trolls, and golems.
Well, that's the poem, all about me.
Now I'm gonna play some video games and feel free.

Enzo Florece (11)
The Cardinal Wiseman Catholic School, Greenford

Purpose

What is our purpose?
We love to our fullest knowing death awaits,
We smile to make others happy,
We exist to find ourselves entangled by society,
What is our purpose?

To live is to experience,
To experience true emotion,
To know love,
To know hate.
We silently scream,
But we continue to love in the hope people will
remember us,
As proof we were there, as proof we mattered.

To live is to understand,
To understand true human nature.
We are curious,
We are bitter,
We are sweet.
Not many people discover this until they are older,
Human life is like an arrow,

It pierces your mind,
Draining your love and draining your compassion,
But we continue living to replace those emotions.

Our purpose is to comprehend nature,
Sounds, smells, tastes, textures,
Are all things we experience,
Doing this causes the mind to excite,
To feel euphoric,
Because we remember.

To memorise, to comprehend,
To understand, to feel emotion,
To know death awaits,
But live your life to the fullest.

That is our purpose...

Panashe Mhembere (11)
The Cardinal Wiseman Catholic School, Greenford

This Is Me, A Little Spark Of Everything

This is me,
A little spark of everything!
From smarts to determination,
To a whole lot of rhyming!
And in this poem, I'll
Tell everything about me,
So, it's time to go, go, go!
'Cause I don't have time, you see.

This is me,
A person with determination!
From work to games,
Even if it comes with aggravation.
No matter what the goal is,
I'll always reach it,
I'll get there in the end,
And won't fall in a despair pit.

This is me,
A living map of the London Underground.

Yes, it is true.
If I'm lying, you can pound me to the ground,
I'll know where you need to go,
All the lines and the stations,
Like at Ealing Broadway, just take the
District Line. And you'll be at South Kensington.

This is me,
A child with more secrets to uncover.
Yet I can't share all of them,
And I might never, ever.
But it was fun to share my poem,
And I really hope you liked it,
'Cause I liked sharing what makes me,
A mixture of everything.

Noah Vita (12)
The Cardinal Wiseman Catholic School, Greenford

What Makes Me?

Turn on your cauldron,
Wait and see,
What ingredients you need to make me.

DT and art,
A great way to start,
Meditation too,
It's great for me and you.

Making things is the key,
To make lots of others including me,
Add lots of adventure.

As you may know,
I don't like to hang it low.
I am friendly, joyful, and kind,
Around me you'll always have the right set of mind.

The school library is the best place I ever knew,
There are books and a puzzle and a lot of other
things to do.

Relax for a moment,
Always could help you and me,

And music and other nice things,
All share the feeling of being happy.

So many other things I like to do,
But they all just won't fit into this stew.

Mix thoroughly and do not tell anyone about this
spell,
It is magical like you and me,
So don't let anyone ever know or see...

Alicja Zywiecka (11)
The Cardinal Wiseman Catholic School, Greenford

Who Am I?

Hi, my name is Gisela, my name means pledge and it's spelt G-I-S-E-L-A.

G stands for grateful, I'm thankful for everything I have.

I stands for independent, but I still have a big group of caring friends who I value.

S stands for sensible, I've always been the sensible one of my friends, but don't underestimate me as I am smiley, sociable, and a bit silly, too.

E stands for extraordinary, it's what my friends call me. I'm not sure I'm worthy, but thanks for the compliment.

L stands for likeable, people say I'm fun to be around.

And last but not least...

A stands for appreciative, like I said, I'm grateful for everything.

So thank you to the people that have loved and supported me.

Grateful, Independent, Sensible, Extraordinary, Likeable, Appreciative, these are the qualities that I pledge to carry on living by.
This is who I am!

Gisela Rodrigues-Ram (12)
The Cardinal Wiseman Catholic School, Greenford

The Adventurer

I woke up on a sunny morning in a joyful mood,
I heard about the hidden treasure and quickly ate some food,
I put on my oversized clothes and took my bag off the hook,
I found the map and put in my big book.

I packed my bag and set out for the wood with my goods,
I heard a creepy sound and was now in a terrifying mood.
I saw a shadow behind the trees.
Nevermind! Just a bunch of bees.

I ran into a dark, gloomy cave.
I wasn't scared anymore, I was very brave.
I saw something glowing gold in the dark.
It was the one and only treasure!

Caywen Estibeiro (12)
The Cardinal Wiseman Catholic School, Greenford

Duty Of A Gamer

Wake up at 6.45 in the morning,
Feeling refreshed and energised,
Without a warning,
No time for yawning,
Mum bursts into my room.

After my eating my fulfilling breakfast,
I turned on my PC,
Ready to play video games,
Or more importantly,
MC (Minecraft).

After fulfilling my duty of a gamer,
My eyes nearly fell shut,
I thought of it as doing the world a favour,
Feeling like the village saviour,
Finally getting off my butt.

Adam Gallagher (11)
The Cardinal Wiseman Catholic School, Greenford

Self-Confidence Girl

I am Flossie,
I am bossy,
When it comes to self-confidence
I have much experience.

'Cause I am a goddess,
I am so flawless,
And when you come up to me,
I'll be like, "Wow! You're so pretty!"

When you come up to me,
I'll be like, "Oui oui,"
'Cause I can speak French
I can teach you some,
If you sit down on that bench.

Flossie O'Meara (11)
The Cardinal Wiseman Catholic School, Greenford

Who Am I?

I have brown hair,
And live without a care,
My life is very busy with dance, but,
I will always be there.
My mind wonders about what people think,
Your opinions matter, but why would you care,
If I like blue or pink.
School is new,
Everyone is different, I haven't got a clue,
Laughing and having fun.
For after all I am myself and I wouldn't rather,
Be anyone else.

Ruby Lynch (11)
The Cardinal Wiseman Catholic School, Greenford

I Am Happy To Be Me

If I could be someone
I know exactly who to be
Unique and different from all
I would choose to be me.

I can't compare myself
With any other girl I see
Because I am not her and
She is not me.

I look in the mirror
And what do I see?
I see the me
No one else can be.

My hair, my face,
My personality.
I am happy
To be me.

Mariam Albazi (11)
The Cardinal Wiseman Catholic School, Greenford

Who Am I?

"Who am I?" I used to ask myself,
But I learnt how to be my true self.
Long hair or short hair,
This isn't fair!
Sad style, happy style,
I've had many trails.
Green eyes, blue eyes,
Brown eyes, grey.
I always felt like the prey.
But now I understand,
I can be myself,
No need for pretty eyes,
No need for more tries.

Maja Adamczyk (11)
The Cardinal Wiseman Catholic School, Greenford

A Wonderful World Beyond My Imagination

My eyes like buttered chocolate with darker rays fanning out
Around the depthless black of an iris,
Swirled with caramel crescent moons,
And trapped by a thick, hazy, black limbal ring.
My chestnut hair swirling,
Like the spiral slide in a funfair.
If each strand of my hair is a star,
My head is its own galaxy.
So really, truly,
This is me.

Scarlett Awad (11)
The Cardinal Wiseman Catholic School, Greenford

Mastermind

He is a mastermind
A genius
He is the best of the best
He is a mastermind.

He makes robots out of steel
They serve him
He has made his own island
He is a mastermind.

Crazier than the President
Crazier than the Joker
Smarter than the best scientist
He is a mastermind.

Ksawian Thisokkumar (12)

The Cardinal Wiseman Catholic School, Greenford

My Swaggy Life

My name is Izabela
I like to eat yogobella
I'm a very good dancer
My favourite reindeer is Prancer

I am so swaggy
So is my granny
I am a goddess
I am so flawless
I have a brother
We share the same mother
we both like turkey
Because we are so quirky.

Izabela Salo (11)
The Cardinal Wiseman Catholic School, Greenford

What Makes Me, Me?

I look in the mirror and what do I see?
I see someone that no one else can be.
I love reading books, it is my favourite thing,
And all the books I read are so interesting.
I love my religion, and I think studying is fun,
I cannot wait to grow up and see what I become.
When people ask me, "What do you love about yourself?"
I reply, "My short brown hair and my hazelnut eyes."
The people I love the most are my siblings,
Because they never fail to show up when I need them the most.
Roses are red, violets are blue,
This is what makes me, me.
So tell me, what makes you, you?

Sara Khan (10)
Winston Way Academy, Ilford

How To Make Me

Ingredients:
- Deep sleeping, 12 tablespoons
- Chocolate loving, 5 teaspoons
- Funniness, 1mg
- Getting distracted, 5g
- Weight, 42.3kg
- Watching films, 1kg
- Indian, 80g
- British, 20g
- Dark brown eyes, 100g
- Wishes, 80 tablespoon
- Spider-Man fan, 100 teaspoon
- Elysian sugar (the magical ingredient that will make you into me), 1 teaspoon
- Conscientious salt, 1 teaspoon.

Instructions:
First get a huge blender,
Then add all the ingredients in the blender
Blend for two minutes.
The paste will be smaller.

Put it in the microwave at 230C for thirty minutes.
You will have peppermints.
Eat it and become me!

Nishwanth Patro (11)
Winston Way Academy, Ilford

A Poem About Me, Only Me!

I am a kid and I'm generous.
I'm not usually scared of most things except snakes and spiders!
My dream is to become an engineer, scientist, and artist.
My future will be to become a prime minister
Because I want to create a peaceful society.
My hobby is art and I like drawing characters and sceneries.
I also strongly believe in my religion too.
I would like to go on adventures and have fun!
The thing I hate is being included in a quarrel and people lying to me.
So that's a poem about me, only me!
What about you?

Dia Zareeta Hossain (10)
Winston Way Academy, Ilford

This Is Part Of My Life

I am a girl, I am unique,
What I do and what I don't do is part of my life.
I am special and I love my family.
I am curious, this is part of my life.
I am brave, but I do get scared.
When I see a spider I creep out,
This is part of my life.
I help my mum with things, but they become worse.
When my mum explains to me how to do it, I understand.
This is part of my life.
I have to study, I am happy that I can learn.
I do good teamwork and I am happy with friends,
This is part of my life.

Aishah Arif (10)
Winston Way Academy, Ilford

This Is Me

My name is Mehdi and I'm nine.
I am a bit shorter, but it's fine.
I like football as I am not tall enough to play basketball.
When I am spending time with my dad,
I am no longer miserable or sad.
I am not hateful as I am loving and grateful.
When I look at the moon,
My heart plays a beautiful tune.
When I see someone fight,
I close my eyes and think that it is not right.
So this is my little and very short sublime rhyme.

Mehdi Shah (10)
Winston Way Academy, Ilford

All About Me!

R is for rainbow, rainbow has colours like my drawing. Not only do I like drawing, I also like playing games and painting pretty pictures.

A is for amazing, watching TV and drawing makes me feel better when I am sad.

I is for ice cream, I eat it when I scream.

N is for name, I am still describing my nice name.

A is for ambition. My dream is to become a doctor.

This is what I want to be, this is all about me!

Raina Morshed (9)

Winston Way Academy, Ilford

This Is Me

I am known as Durva,
Which means an auspicious offering.
When I grow up, I have the dream to teach.
My heart yearns for the act of a teacher.
The thought of teaching youthful children,
Brings immense joy to me.
Seeing the smiles of these children,
Makes me aspire, more and more.
In the future, I really hope
I will be a wonderful teacher.

Durva Kore (9)
Winston Way Academy, Ilford

Who Am I?

Every day I wake up and ask myself,
Who am I? I say that I'm a girl
That can never be replaced.
I am a girl who loves herself,
I am a girl who is helpful.
I am a girl who is happy.
I am a girl with hope.
I am a girl who doesn't give up.
I am a girl who never stops thinking about how the future is going to be
And how the past was.

Zara Gir (10)
Winston Way Academy, Ilford

Amazing Nature

Nature is as beautiful as the Eiffel Tower,
Nature is like the sun in the sky,
Nature is as good as vegetables,
Nature is like flowers in the world,
Nature is as honest as God in Heaven,
Nature is as pleasant as a green place,
Nature is as pure as a crystal and let's preserve it!

Abhinav Bharanitharan (9)
Winston Way Academy, Ilford

This Is Me!

I am Vaibhav

I like green **v** egetables

I am **a** ctive like a honey bee

I am **i** nterested to draw and paint

I want to **b** ecome a chess master

I am **h** appy hanging with my dad

I am **a** ngry when I lose

I'd love to see a **v** irus-free world.

Vaibhav Sriram (7)

Winston Way Academy, Ilford

The Future Oracle

As I looked through the future oracle,
I fell into the future.
That's how it started.
There were jet planes littered in the sky,
And lots of things to buy.
People walking home,
And into a theatre like a dome.
But litter scattered on the floor,
And smoke from planes,
Soon might destroy this world.

Agastya Sinha (8)
Winston Way Academy, Ilford

This Is Me

I am creative and smart.
I wonder what will happen in the future.
I want to eat some tart.
I worry if I'm not good at my goal.
I am creative and smart.
I understand why we all have a nose with two holes.
I say we never give up.
I dream I can go into space.
I am creative and smart.

Diyaab Rizwan (9)
Winston Way Academy, Ilford

Helpful Me

H elping you to do something
E ncouraging all the way
L earning to help each other
P ractically helping when needed
F ully helping you
U seful when you need help
L oving all your ideas.

Mariam Ridita (9)
Winston Way Academy, Ilford

YOUNG WRITERS INFORMATION

We hope you have enjoyed reading this book – and that you will continue to in the coming years.

If you're the parent or family member of an enthusiastic poet or story writer, do visit our website **www.youngwriters.co.uk/subscribe** and sign up to receive news, competitions, writing challenges and tips, activities and much, much more! There's lots to keep budding writers motivated!

If you would like to order further copies of this book, or any of our other titles, then please give us a call or order via your online account.

Young Writers
Remus House
Coltsfoot Drive
Peterborough
PE2 9BF
(01733) 890066
info@youngwriters.co.uk

Join in the conversation!
Tips, news, giveaways and much more!

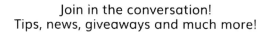
 **YoungWritersUK**  **YoungWritersCW** 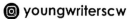 **youngwriterscw**